Contents

C000151922

Introduction

The Mental Warm-up Activities provide a structured scheme of work for developing mental mathematics strategies. The daily activities have been written to practise key mental maths skills, and address these using a variety of techniques:

- practising pre-requisite skills (e.g. partitioning numbers: 8 is 7 and 1, 6 and 2, 5 and 3, 4 and 4)
- building on two or more of these skills to develop a new strategy (e.g. adding 17 + 8 by partitioning 8 into 3 and 5, and knowing that 17 + 3 = 20)
- practising and extending known strategies (e.g. 127 + 8 =)
- using known strategies as pre-requisites for a new set of strategies, (e.g. related to a different operation)
- developing a 'memory bank' of key facts (e.g. addition bonds to 10, doubles to 10)
- using key facts to develop further strategies (e.g. 6 + 6 = 12 so 6 + 7 = 13).

How to use the book

To allow the teacher flexibility, the book is broken down into two sections:

Unit specific activities

For each Number Unit there are two whole class activities. Some of these relate directly to skills or sub-skills for that Unit. Some activities practise more general skills, and these will develop in strands throughout the book (a skills chart mapping this development is included on pages vi to viii). Often the activities provided will be enough to cover the work required for that Unit.

Activity Bank

For Number Units that last longer than two days, or for Shape, Data and Measures Units, the teacher can select supplementary activities from the bank provided at the back of the book. The Activity Bank includes a wide variety of activities that address key skills. The activities in the bank can be used at any time alongside any topic and often you will wish to revisit them throughout the year.

Together these two types of activity will provide enough activities for one warm-up each day.

The activities in this book are of three types:

Open-ended
These are activities where there may be several ways of getting a 'right' answer. Often a key benefit of the activity will be the discussion which the children have with you and each other about which strategies they have used. This is a good opportunity to go through several different ways of doing something with the whole class, so that different methods or techniques are shared and discussed.

Closed
These activities have one correct answer and, usually, one preferred strategy to use. So, for example, when adding 9 to a 2-digit number, the activity may practise the specific technique of adding 10 and taking one away.

Memorising
These activities are designed to help children memorise a particular set of number facts, e.g. doubles of numbers to 10, addition bonds. Eventually each child will have a set of memorised facts that they know by heart. Certain key activities appear several times during the book to help reinforce these skills.

Generic activities
Most of the activities use similar formats and structures from Unit to Unit, and children will become familiar with these. These 'generic' activities are described in more detail on pages iv to v.

Also included in each section are a word of the week, a number of the week or a shape of the week. These can be used to develop children's use of the language and vocabulary of number, both spoken ('tell me something about this week's number') and written ('write three things about this week's shape').

The number of the week can be used to develop mental dexterity, consolidate concepts and skills studied in a given Number Unit, and to develop the use and understanding of the language of number. For each number some sample tasks and facts are given.

The shape of the week can be used to increase awareness of the properties of shape and space, and to encourage the use of the associated language.

The word of the week can be used to develop the use and understanding of the vocabulary of mathematics, and to consolidate language associated with the Unit being studied. Sometimes the 'word of the week' relates to vocabulary in the relevant Unit, sometimes the word is included to rehearse vocabulary met in the past. Children should be encouraged both to hear the word being used in different contexts, and to use the word in responses and statements.

Working partners

At beginning of the year (or each term), place the children in pairs (or threes) as 'working partners'. The pairs do not necessarily have to be matched by ability – two children of different abilities can sometimes help each other. Over time the children will become used to working together, and a 'regular' partner will save you time when setting up the activities.

Generic Activities

Many of the activities throughout this book follow common formats and structures. This will enable you quickly to set up and run a particular activity, and over time, the children will become used to the 'rules' involved. The 'generic' activities are described here in more detail.

Roundabout counting
- Write ten starter numbers on the board.
- Point to a number. The children count on as a class in steps set by you (e.g. ones, tens).
- Point to a different number. The children count on, one at a time. Point to children at random for them to continue the count.

Match me
- The teacher has a set of number cards. Pupils have their own sets.
- Hold up a card. Read it aloud.
- Pupils perform some operation on the teacher's card and hold up the matching answer.

Round the class
- Write ten starter numbers on the board.
- Point to a number and say a child's name.
- That child performs some operation on the number and says the answer.
- If incorrect, choose another child.
- If correct, the first child chooses a second child and selects a new number.
- Continue like this around the class.

Missing numbers
- Write six sequences of numbers on the board, each with several numbers missing.
- Point to a missing number and choose one or several children to say which number it is.
- Repeat for each missing number.

Open the box
- Draw a grid on the board and write a number in each space.

- Cover each number with a piece of Blu-tacked card. Write a number on the card that relates in some way to the number beneath (e.g. ten more, double).
- Choose a child to choose a card and perform some operation on the number.
- Reveal the answer by removing the card.

Bingo
- The children work with their partners. They write five 'bingo' numbers on a piece of paper, circling each one. The numbers should match a certain criterion (e.g. a 2-digit number).
- The teacher generates numbers at random (e.g. by selecting cards from a shuffled set).
- The teacher chooses a child to perform an operation on the card (e.g. rounding to the next ten).
- The children can cross out one of their 'bingo' numbers if it matches the answer.
- The first pair to cross out all their numbers wins.

How many?
- The children work with their partners.
- Write a series of numbers on the board.
- The children have a given amount of time to combine the numbers using different operations to make a target number.
- Discuss the different methods.

Grid operations
- Draw a grid on the board and write a number in each space.
- The children copy the empty grid, performing an operation on each number before entering it in their grid.
- Go through the grid on the board, asking different children for their answers.

Right and wrong
- Write several additions, subtractions, multiplications or divisions on the board, one of which is incorrect.
- The children work with their partners to decide which is incorrect.
- Allow a set time.
- For some activities you may want to demonstrate a particular mental technique, before children start the activity.

Skills chart

The following chart outlines the mental skills addressed by the Mental Warm-up activities (the activities in the Activity Bank are listed separately, on pages 44 to 45).

The skills are divided into different areas: counting, addition, subtraction etc. The chart will assist any teacher looking for an activity dealing with a specific skill. It also makes clear the build-up and sequence of concepts covered throughout the book.

Topic	Specific Skills	Units
Counting, place-value, ordering, rounding	Counting in ones from a 2- or 3-digit number	N1
	Counting in ones from a 3-digit number	N1
	Counting in ones from a 2- or 3-digit number	N7, N18
	Counting in tens from a 3-digit number	N8, N15, N18, N34
	Counting in hundreds from a 3-digit number	N35
	Counting back in tens from 2- and 3-digit numbers	N31
	Counting in twos	N22, N39
	Counting in twos to 20 or 30	N10
	Counting in tens and twenties	N21
	Counting in tens (up to 100)	N8
	Counting in tens and fives	N13
	Counting in fifties	N21
	Counting in hundreds, tens, units	N36
	Ordering 2-digit numbers	N15
	Ordering 3-digit numbers	N2, N29
	Place-value in 3-digit numbers	N7, N14
	Rounding 2-digit numbers to the nearest ten	N29
	Even and odd numbers	N22, N36

Fractions	Finding quarters and eighths	N28
	Halves, quarters, thirds	N41

Mental calculation strategies (addition and subtraction)	Addition pairs to 10	N3
	Addition pairs to 7, 8, 9	N3, N5
	Addition pairs to 20	N4
	Addition pairs to 100 (multiples of 5)	N23, N30
	Addition pairs and triplets to 10	N5
	Addition pairs and triplets to 10	N5
	Adding to make the next ten	N16, N17, N32
	Adding three 1-digit numbers	N43
	Adding and subtracting 1-digit numbers	N9
	Adding ten or fifteen to 2-digit numbers	N13
	Adding multiples of five	N14
	Adding tens and multiples of ten	N19, N30
	Adding and subtracting multiples of ten	N19
	Adding multiples of ten to 2-digit numbers	N20
	Adding three multiples of ten	N43
	Adding and subtracting nine to and from 2-digit numbers	N20
	Adding 9 or 19 to a 2-digit number	N42
	Adding 9, 19, 29, 39 to a 2-digit number	N33
	Adding 21, 32, 43 to a 3-digit number	N42
	Adding 2-digit numbers	N23, N33
	Adding 50 to a 3-digit number	N35
	Adding 1-digit and 2-digit numbers	N34
	Adding near doubles	N16, N27
	Difference	N32
	Subtraction by counting on	N17
	Subtracting 1-digit numbers	N6
	Subtracting to make a multiple of ten	N6
	Subtracting two 2-digit numbers	N31

Mental calculation strategies (multiplication and division)	Doubles of numbers to 12	N11
	Doubling numbers up to 30	N24
	Doubling	N9, N12, N24, N39
	Halving even numbers up to 20	N11, N12, N28
	Halving	N41
	×5 and ×10 multiplication facts, addition	N37
	×5 and ×10 multiplication facts	N25
	×5 multiplication facts	N26
	Multiplying by 5	N25
	×10 and ×100 multiplication facts	N38
	Multiplying by 10	N37
	×3 multiplication facts	N27
	×3 division facts	N40
	Multiplication facts up to 6×6	N26, N40
	Multiplication facts up to 10×10	N38
	Adding, subtracting and multiplying 1-digit numbers	N10

N1 Place-value

Roundabout counting

Counting in ones from a 2- or 3-digit number
Write five 2-digit and five 3-digit starter
numbers on the board.
Point to a starter number.
Count on in ones as a class.
Point to a new starter number.
Count on in ones, pointing at
random to different children
who say the next number in
the count.

Missing numbers

Counting in ones from a 3-digit number
Write six sequences of consecutive 3-digit numbers on the board, each
with some numbers missing.
Point to a missing number and choose a child to say what it is.
Repeat for each missing number.

Number of the week

Sample tasks	• Read the number.
	• How many units, tens, hundreds in the number?
	• Count forwards/backwards in ones or tens from the number.
Sample facts	• it is even
	• it is 6 more than 250
	• it is between 200 and 300
	• its tens digit is 3 more than its hundreds digit

N2 Place-value

Open the box

Ordering 3-digit numbers

Draw a 4 × 2 grid on the board. Cover each space with a blank card, and underneath write a 3-digit number. Choose a child to reveal a number and read it aloud. Check with the class. When all the numbers are

revealed the children work in pairs to write all the numbers in order.

Stick there

Place-value in 3-digit numbers

Two dice and cubes

Divide the class into two teams. Write 'H, T and U' on the board for each team. The teams take turns to throw the dice and write the number on the board in the hundreds, the tens or the units column. They are trying to make the largest number they can.

When each team has a 3-digit number they all read it aloud.

Which number is larger? That team collects a cube.

Continue until one team has seven cubes.

Word of the week

Sample tasks
- How many digits in the number 156?
- What is the value of the hundreds digit in 587?

Sample facts
- a number between 10 and 100 has two digits
- a million has seven digits
- a digit is another word for finger

N3 Addition

Grid addition

Addition pairs to 10
Draw a 5 × 2 grid on the board, with a number (1 to 10) in each space.
The children copy the grid, writing the number pair to 10.
They should try to keep up with you as you write the numbers.
When the grid is complete, point to each space in turn, asking a
different child to say their answer.

Match me

Addition pairs to 7, 8, 9
Number cards (0 to 9), one set per pair
Select a card at random from a set
(0 to 7), hold it up and read it aloud.
Children should hold up the number pair
to 7.
Repeat for pairs to 8 and 9.

Number of the week

Sample tasks
- Say a pair which add to make the number.
- Say three numbers which add to make our number.
- Say the number which makes our number (10) with 3, 8, 4, ...
- Say a pair which differ by our number.

Sample facts
- it is 3 and 7, 4 and 6, ...
- it is half of 20, a quarter of 40, ...
- it is the first 2-digit number

 N4 Addition

Bingo

Addition pairs to 20

Number cards (0 to 20)
Each pair writes five bingo
numbers that are between
0 and 20.
Select a card at random, hold it
up and say it aloud.
Choose a child to say the pair
to 20.
Any pair with the matching number
can cross it out.

Missing numbers

Addition pairs to 20

Number cards (1 to 20), coins.
Divide the class into four teams: '1p', '2p', '5p', '10p'. Write their names
on the board next to a picture of the appropriate coin.
Take a card and choose a child to match it, using the minimum number
of coins, e.g. 6p (5p + 1p). *What goes with that amount to make 20p?*
Agree the answer with the class, and the fewest coins you need to make
it. The teams score one point for each time their coin is used.
Repeat.

Shape of the week

square

Sample facts
• it is a flat (2-d) shape
• it has 4 sides, all the same length
• it has 4 lines of symmetry
• it has 4 right angles
• it is used to measure area

N5 Addition

Pairs

Addition pairs to 7, 8 and 9

Several sets of number cards (0 to 7, or 0 to 8, or 0 to 9), enough for one card per pair

Give each pair a card. The pairs arrange themselves in groups of four, so that their two number cards total 7. Write all the pairs on the board in order.

Repeat using cards (0 to 8) and making 8 or using cards (0 to 9) and making 9.

Missing numbers

Addition pairs and triplets to 10

Write ten additions on the board, each making 10, and with one or more missing numbers.

Point to a missing number and ask all the children to hold up fingers to match. Repeat for each missing number.

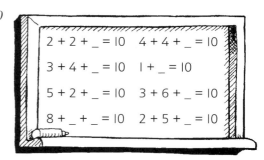

$$2 + 2 + \_ = 10 \qquad 4 + 4 + \_ = 10$$
$$3 + 4 + \_ = 10 \qquad 1 + \_ = 10$$
$$5 + 2 + \_ = 10 \qquad 3 + 6 + \_ = 10$$
$$8 + \_ + \_ = 10 \qquad 2 + 5 + \_ = 10$$

Number of the week

9

Sample tasks
- Say a pair which add to make our number.
- Say three numbers which add to make our number.
- Add our number to 12, 23, 46, ...

Sample facts
- it is 1 less than 10
- it can be added by adding 10, then taking away 1
- it is the fifth odd number

N6 Subtraction

Match me

Subtracting to make a multiple of ten
Number cards (1 to 9), one set per child
Select two number cards at random to
make a 2-digit number. Hold up the
cards and say the number.
Children hold up the number that
needs to be subtracted to leave a
multiple of ten.

How many?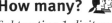

Subtracting 1-digit numbers
Number cards (5 to 9)
Deal one card to each pair. How many subtractions can they find that
start with their number?
Allow three minutes.
Discuss the different answers.

Word of the week

estimate

Sample tasks
- Estimate the length of your pencil.
- Estimate how heavy this book is.
- Estimate how many chairs in the classroom.

Sample facts
- an estimate is a guess using things we know
- the estimate of an answer can be made by rounding
  numbers

N7 Numbers to 1000

Missing numbers

Counting in tens from a 2-digit number
Write a sequence of 2-digit numbers
on the board, rising in tens with
some missing.
Point to a missing number and
choose a child to say what it is.
Check with the class.
Repeat for each missing number.
Repeat, including some sequences
of 3-digit numbers.

Target numbers

Place-value in 3-digit numbers
A dice
Divide the class into two teams, 'Lions' and 'Tigers'. Write '451' on the
board, as a target. Draw two HTU grids below it. Choose a child from the
'Lions' to throw the dice and place the number on the grid, i.e. in the
Hundreds, the Tens or the Units. They are trying to make a number
which is as close as possible to 451. Repeat this process, choosing a child
from the 'Tigers'.
Continue until both grids are complete. Whose number is closest to the
target?

Number of the week

Sample tasks
- Say a number which is more/less than this number.
- Say the number which is 10 more/10 less/100
  more/100 less.
- Say two numbers which our number lies between.
- Say a number which is less and has
  5 tens/4 hundreds.

Sample facts
- it is odd and nearly 440
- it is 10 less than 447/100 more than 337
- it is between 400 and 500

N8 Numbers to 1000

Roundabout counting

Counting in tens (up to 100)
Write ten 1- and 2-digit starter numbers on the board.
Point to a starter number. Count on in tens as a class.
Point to a new starter number. Count on in tens, pointing at random to different children who say the next number in the count.

Target counting

Counting in tens from a 3-digit number
A dice
Write a 3-digit target number on the board.
Throw the dice twice to give the hundreds and tens of the starting number (the units should match the target number). Try to ensure the starter and target are not too distant from each other.
Children decide whether to count on or back.
Count in tens in unison up or down to the target.
Repeat, counting around the class, with each child saying the next number. The child who says the target number can choose the next target.

Shape of the week

Sample facts
- it is a solid (3-d) shape
- it has 6 faces which are all squares
- it has 8 corners (vertices)
- it has 12 edges, all the same length

N9 Multiplication/division

How many?

Adding and subtracting 1-digit numbers
Write '5, 6, 7, 8, 9' on the board.
The children use addition and/or subtraction to combine two or more of the numbers to make a final answer of 10, e.g. $8 + 9 - 7 = 10$.
Allow ten minutes.
Discuss the different answers.

Bingo

Doubling
Number cards (1 to 10)
Each pair writes five bingo numbers (which are even numbers between 1 and 20).
Select a card at random, hold it up, and say it aloud.
Choose a pair of children to double the number.
Any pair with the matching answer can cross it out.

Number of the week

Sample tasks
• Count in 2s to/from our number.
• How many is our number of 2s (i.e. 8×2)?
• Double/halve our number.

Sample facts
• it is double 4/four 2s/two 4s, ...
• it is the fourth even number
• it is the number of: sides of an octagon/legs of an octopus

N10 Multiplication/division

Larger and smaller

Adding, subtracting and multiplying 1-digit numbers
Write the numbers '2, 3, 5, 6' on the board.
The children work in pairs to try to make the largest possible total by
adding, subtracting or multiplying the four numbers. Allow them five
minutes, then discuss the different totals and methods.
Repeat, asking the children to make the smallest possible total.

Missing numbers

Counting in twos to 20 or 30
Write six sequences of numbers on the board, going up or down in twos,
each with several numbers missing.
Point to a missing number and choose a child to say what it is.
Repeat for each missing number.

Shape of the week

> **cuboid**

Sample facts
- it is a box shape
- it has 6 faces which are squares or rectangles
- it has 8 corners (or vertices)
- it has 12 edges
- most bricks and boxes are cuboids

N11 Multiplication/division

Bingo

Doubling numbers up to 12

Number cards (1 to 12)

Each pair writes five bingo numbers
that are multiples of 2 (up to 24).
Select a card at random, hold it up
and say it aloud, e.g. 4.
Choose a child to double the number
and say the answer, i.e. eight.
Any pair with the matching number
can cross it out.

Circle numbers

Halving even numbers up to 20

Write ten even numbers on the board (up to 20) and circle each one.
Choose a child who says half of one of the numbers.
Choose a child to say which circle number the first child halved.
This can be played as a game, with the class in two teams. Team A halves
a number, Team B guesses which number was halved.

Word of the week

Sample tasks
- What is double 9?
- What number do you have to double to make 24?
- What happens if you double a number, then halve the answer?

Sample facts
- a double of a number is twice the number
- doubles are always even numbers
- double fifty is one hundred

N12 Fractions

Grid numbers

Doubling

Draw a 2 by 5 grid on the board. The children copy the grid.
Write these numbers in order along the top row: 2, 10, 14, 5, 20. The
children double each number and write the answer in the matching
space on their grid. They should try to keep up with you!
Repeat for the bottom row, writing the numbers: 4, 15, 40, 16, 52.
When the grid is complete point to each space in turn, asking a different
child to say their answer. The children can mark their own grids.

Right and wrong

Halving even numbers up to 20

Write six fraction sentences on the board, one
of which is incorrect.
Allow children five minutes to decide which
sentence is incorrect.

$$\frac{1}{2} \text{ of } 10 = 5$$

$$\frac{1}{2} \text{ of } 14 = 7$$

$$\frac{1}{2} \text{ of } 16 = 6$$

$$\frac{1}{2} \text{ of } 8 = 4$$

$$\frac{1}{2} \text{ of } 18 = 9$$

Number of the week

16

Sample tasks
- Continue halving, starting with our number (16, 8, 4, 2, 1, $\frac{1}{2}$, $\frac{1}{4}$, ...).
- Count in 2s/4s to/from our number.
- Say pairs which add to make our number, e.g. 12 + 4, 11 + 5, ...

Sample facts
- it is the even number between 14 and 18
- $\frac{1}{4}$ of our number is 4, $\frac{1}{8}$ of our number is 2, ...
- it is eight 2s, four 4s, ...

N13 Addition/subtraction

Roundabout counting

Counting in tens and fives

Cubes

Write ten 2-digit starter numbers on the board (multiples of 5 or 10). Point to a number. Count in unison in tens. Stop the count and count back in tens to the starter number.

Point to a new starter number. Point at random to different children who say the next number in the count. Count back in tens in the same way.

Repeat for different target numbers, extending to counting in fives.

If a child says a number with a '9', they take a cube (e.g. 95).

Grid addition

Adding ten or fifteen to 2-digit numbers

Draw a 5 × 2 grid on the board, with a 2- or 3-digit number in each space.

Children copy the grid, adding ten or fifteen (you choose) to each number.

When the grid is complete, point to each space in turn, asking a different child to say their answer.

Word of the week

symmetry

Sample tasks
- Draw a line of symmetry on this shape.
- Does this shape have a line of symmetry?
- Complete this drawing so that it has symmetry about this line.

Sample facts
- a fold line is a line of symmetry if one side folds exactly onto the other
- a square has 4 lines of symmetry
- this triangle does not have symmetry

 **Addition**

Target numbers

Place-value in 3-digit numbers

A dice

Divide the class into two teams, 'Lions' and 'Tigers'. Write '531' on the board, as a target. Draw two HTU grids below it. Choose a child from the 'Lions' to throw the dice and place the number on the grid, i.e. in the Hundreds, the Tens or the Units. They are trying to make a number which is as close as possible to 531. Repeat this process, choosing a child from the 'Tigers'.

Continue until both grids are complete. Whose number is closest to the target?

How many?

Adding multiples of five

Write '5, 10, 15, 20, 25, 30, … 50' on the board.

The children can add two or more of the multiples to make 100.

Allow ten minutes.

Discuss the different answers.

Word of the week

centimetre

Sample tasks
- How many centimetres in a metre?
- Estimate the length of your book in centimetres.
- How many centimetres can you jump?
- Find two things that you estimate are 10 centimetres long.

Sample facts
- a centimetre is a small measure of length
- a ruler is 30 centimetres long
- there are 10 centimetres in a decimetre/100 centimetres in a metre

N15 Place-value

Number guess

Ordering 2-digit numbers

Choose a child to write a 2-digit target number, hidden from the others.
At random point to a child who says a 2-digit number.
The first child must say 'larger' or 'smaller'.
Continue until someone
guesses the target number.
This child selects the next
number.

People numbers

Counting in tens from a 3-digit number

Stick a 3-digit target number on the back of one child.
Write a number approximately 150 less on the board (with the same
number of units).
Start counting in tens as a class from the number on the board.
Stop when you reach the target number. The first child writes the
number on the board.
Compare with the target. Are they correct?
Extend to counting in hundreds.

Number of the week

Sample tasks
- Round the number to its nearest ten/hundred.
- How far is it away from its nearest ten/hundred?
- Which other numbers round to the same nearest ten/hundred?

Sample facts
- it is nearly 240
- it is 7 more than 230/3 less than 240
- it is 37 more than 200/63 less than 300

N16 Addition

Match me

Adding to make the next ten

Number cards (1 to 9), one set per pair

Write the number pairs to 10 on the board.

Select two number cards at random to make a 2-digit number. Hold it up and say the number.

Children hold up the number that needs to be added to make the next ten.

Keep a lively pace.

Open the box

Adding near doubles

Draw a 5 × 2 grid. Cover each space with a near double addition (e.g. 25 + 26), and underneath write the answer.

Choose a child to point to a box and say the answer.

Check with the class.

The child can 'open the box' to reveal the answer.

Shape of the week

Sample facts
- a ball is a sphere
- its surface is curved
- it has symmetry – it can be sliced into two matching halves
- half a sphere is called a hemisphere

N17 Addition/subtraction

Bingo

Adding to make the next ten

Number cards (10 to 100)

Each pair writes five bingo numbers between 0 and 10.
Choose a child to take a card at random. Read out the number, e.g. 46.
What is the next multiple of ten? Fifty. How many must we add to get there? Four. Any pair with the matching answer can cross it out.

Right and wrong

Subtraction by counting on

Write '23 – 17 =' on the board.
Choose a child.
How many from 17 to 20? Three. How many from 20 to 23? Three. So the answer is ... six.
Write six subtractions on the board, one of which is incorrect.
Allow children five minutes to decide which subtraction is incorrect.

$$24 - 18 = 6$$

$$32 - 29 = 3$$

$$22 - 17 = 4$$

$$25 - 7 = 18$$

Word of the week

difference

Sample tasks
- Estimate the difference in height between John and Kati.
- What is the difference between 5p and 12p?
- Tell me two numbers which have a difference of 6.

Sample facts
- 4 and 10 have a difference of 6, and a total of 14
- these two towers have a difference in height of 4 cubes
- the difference in length between my foot and yours is about 4 centimetres

N18 Money

Missing numbers

Counting in tens from a 3-digit number

Write five sequences of 3-digit numbers (rising or falling in tens) on the board, each with some numbers missing.

Divide the class into 3 teams. Point to a missing number and choose a team to say what it is.

Repeat for each missing number.

Roundabout counting

Counting on in tens from 2- or 3-digit numbers

Interlocking cubes

Write ten amounts of money on the board, £2.45, £6.24, £1.99 etc.

Point to an amount. Count on in unison, adding 10p each time.

Point to a new amount. Count on in tens, pointing at random to different children who say the next number in the count. If a child bridges through a pound (e.g. from £6.94 to £7.04) they collect a cube (they can choose a friend to help them and both collect a cube).

Repeat, counting back in tens.

Number of the week

Sample tasks
- Say a pair which add to make the number.
- Say the number which makes our number (20) with 13, 6, 17, ...
- Say a pair which make our number and have a difference of 8.

Sample facts
- it is 5 + 15, 18 + 2, ...
- it is double 10
- it is ten twos, four fives, ...
- it is half of 40

N19 Addition/subtraction

Missing number

Adding tens and multiples of ten

Number grid (1 to 100), displayed where the children can see it

Write ten additions on the board, each adding a multiple of ten (which is missing). Divide the class into 3 teams. Point to a missing number and choose a team to say what it is. Repeat for each missing number.

Open the box

Adding and subtracting multiples of ten

Draw a 5×2 grid on the board. Cover each space with a 2- or 3-digit number (e.g. 354), and underneath the number 50 more (i.e. 404). Choose a child to point to a box and say the number 50 more. Check with the class. The child can 'open the box' to reveal the answer. Repeat for adding 30 or subtracting 40.

Number of the week

Sample tasks	• Which numbers round to 50 as their nearest ten?
	• Add our number to 21, 32, 47, 16, ...
	• Say the number which makes our number (50) with 20, 35, 14, ...
Sample facts	• it is five 10s, ten 5s, two 25s, ...
	• it is 10 + 40, 20 + 30, 5 + 45, ...
	• it is half of 100/a half century
	• it is the score for a bull's-eye in darts

N20 Addition/subtraction

Number guess

Adding multiples of ten to 2-digit numbers

A dice

Each child writes a 2-digit number.

Throw the dice. Choose a child to add that many tens to their number and say the result aloud. Choose another child to guess what the original number was.

If correct, that child completes the next addition.

Right and wrong

Adding and subtracting nine to and from 2-digit numbers

Write '26 + 9 =' on the board.

Choose a child.

Add nine by adding ten and taking one away.

First add ten to 26. Thirty-six. Then take one away. Thirty-five.

Write six additions and subtractions on the board, one of which is incorrect.

Allow children five minutes to decide which addition is incorrect.

Word of the week

Sample tasks
- Estimate the width of the room in metres.
- How many centimetres in half a metre?
- Find two objects that are about one metre long.

Sample facts
- a metre is a large measure of length
- a metre ruler measures lengths in metres
- a metre is slightly longer than a yard
- sprinters run races which are 100 metres long

(N21) Counting

Roundabout counting

Counting in tens and twenties

Write ten starter numbers that are 3-digit multiples of 10 on the board.
Point to a starter number. Count on in tens as a class.
Point to a new starter number. Count on in tens, pointing at random to different children who say the next number in the count.
Extend to counting in twenties. Help the children bridge a hundred by writing the numbers on the board (e.g. 290, 310).

Bingo

Counting in fifties

Number cards (1 to 20)

Each pair writes five multiples of fifty between 50 and 1000.
Select a card at random, e.g. 13. Starting at 50 count on by that many fifties, e.g. 50, 100, 150, 200, 250, 300, 350, 400, 450, 500, 550, 600, 650. Write the numbers on the board. Point to the last number. Any pair with a matching number can cross it out.

Number of the week

4316

Sample tasks
- Read our number, read the number 1 more/1 less.
- Count on/back in 1s, 10s, 100s from our number.
- What is the hundreds digit, the units digit, ...?

Sample facts
- it is between 4000 and 5000
- it is a 4-digit number
- its digits total 14

Four thousand three hundred and sixteen,
Four thousand three hundred and twenty six...

N22 Odd and even

Round the class

Counting in twos

Write ten even 2-digit numbers on the board.

Point to a number and say a child's name. That child must say the number two more. If correct that child chooses another to say the number two more again. Continue around the class.

After several turns, start again with a new different number.

Team winners

Even and odd numbers

Number cards (10 to 50)

Divide the class into two teams: 'evens' and 'odds'.

Shuffle the cards and place them face down in a pile. One child from each team selects a card. Choose a child to add the two numbers. If the answer is even, the 'even' team score a point. If it is odd the 'odd' team score a point.

Play ten rounds.

Number of the week

Sample tasks
- Say the odd numbers, in order, up to/beyond our number.
- Is double our number odd or even?
- What must be added to our number to make 30, 40, 50, 100, ...?

Sample facts
- it is the second odd number after 20
- its digits are in order (consecutive)
- its nearest 10 is 20

Ⓝ23 Addition/subtraction

Number guess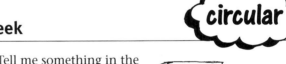

Addition pairs to 100 (multiples of 5)
Each pair writes a 2-digit multiple of five, e.g. 15, 20, 25, … hidden from everyone else.
Choose a pair, who say what must be added to their number to make 100. The other children guess their original number.
Continue for different pairs.

How many?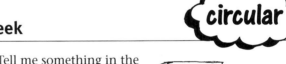

Adding two 2-digit numbers
Write the numbers '12, 15, 22, 24, 25, 38, 76' on the board.
The pairs make as many different multiples of 10 as they can using any or all of these numbers, using addition and subtraction. How many can they make in 6 minutes?

Word of the week

circular

Sample tasks
- Tell me something in the room which is circular.
- Draw a circular face.

Sample facts
- the edge of a disc is circular
- the flower bed is circular
- squares and rectangles are not circular

Grid doubling

Doubling numbers up to 30 (less than 5 units)

Draw a 5×2 grid on the board, with a 2-digit number (less than 5 units) in each space.

Children copy the grid, doubling each number before writing them in the grid.

When the grid is complete, point to each space in turn, asking a different child to say their answer.

Bingo

Doubling

Number cards (5, 10, 15, ... 50)

Each pair writes three multiples of 10.

Select a card at random and hold it up. Choose a child to double it. Any pair with the matching double can cross it out.

Number of the week

Sample tasks
- Count in 5s forwards to/backwards from our number.
- How many 5s/10s make our number?
- Continue halving from our number, i.e. 40, 20, 10, 5, $2\frac{1}{2}$, ...

Sample facts
- it is double 20/four 10s/eight 5s, ...
- it is 10 + 30, 20 + 20, ...
- it is the nearest 10 to 37, to 41, to 44, ...

(N25) Multiplication/division

Open the box

×5 and ×10 multiplication facts

Draw a 4 × 2 grid. Cover each space with a 1-digit number (e.g. 7), and underneath write the matching multiple of 5 (i.e. 35).

Choose a child to point to a box and multiply by 5. Check with the class.

The child can 'open the box' to reveal the answer.

Repeat for multiplying by 10.

Guess the number

Multiplying by five

Write a 3-digit number on the board with five units, e.g. 435. Each pair makes an estimate of what must be multiplied by 5 to make 435. Write their estimates on the board, then reveal the answer (87). Who was closest? That pair chooses the next 3-digit number.

Words of the week

row/column

Sample tasks   Look at the large number grid:
- Tell me the numbers in the second row.
- Which number is in the fourth row and fifth column?
- Draw a rectangle on your squared paper which has 6 rows and 8 columns.

Sample facts
- rows go across, columns go down
- a 3 by 7 grid has 3 rows and 7 columns
- a square grid has the same number of rows as columns
- you sit in rows at the cinema

Multiplication/division

Grid multiplication

×5 multiplication facts
Draw a 3×4 grid on the board, with a number (up to 12) in each space.
Children copy the grid, multiplying each number by 5.
When the grid is complete, point to each space in turn, asking a
different child to say their answer.

Right and wrong

Multiplication facts up to 6×6
Write six multiplications on the
board, one of which is incorrect.
Allow children five minutes to
decide which multiplication is
incorrect.

$3 \times 4 = 12$ $4 \times 6 = 22$

$5 \times 2 = 10$ $2 \times 4 = 8$

$6 \times 3 = 18$ $5 \times 3 = 15$

Number of the week

24

Sample tasks
- Count in 2s/3s/4s/6s forwards/backwards to/from our number.
- How many 2s/3s/4s/6s make our number?
- Continue halving from our number, i.e. 24, 12, 6, 3, $1\frac{1}{2}$, …
- What is a half/a quarter of our number?

Sample facts
- it is four 6s, eight 3s, …
- it is 2 dozen
- it is 20 + 4, 28 – 4, 30 – 6, …

N27 Multiplication/division

Grid addition

Adding near doubles
Draw a 10×2 grid on the board, with a near double addition (e.g. 14 + 15) in each space.
Children copy the grid, writing the answer to each addition.
When the grid is complete, point to each space in turn, asking a different child to say their answer.

Missing numbers

×3 multiplication facts
Write ten ×3 facts on the board, each with a missing number.
Point to a missing number and choose a child to say what it is.
Repeat for each missing number.

$2 \times 3 = \_$

$\_ \times 3 = 15$

$\_ \times 3 = 12$

Number of the week

Sample tasks
- Count in 3s from our number. How far can you go?
- What is five 3s, three 3s, ten 3s, ...?
- How many 3s in 15, 21, 12, ...?

Sample facts
- it is the number of sides/corners (vertices) of a triangle
- it is half of 6, a quarter of 12, ...
- it is the second odd number

Ⓝ28 Fractions

Open the box

Halving numbers to 20
Draw a 5 × 2 grid on the board. Cover each space with an even number, and underneath write its half.
Choose a child to point to a box and say half. Check with the class.
The child can 'open the box' to reveal the answer.

Circle numbers

Finding quarters and eighths
Write '32, 20, 16, 24, 40, 28', on the board, circling each one.
Divide the class into 4 teams. Choose a team to say one quarter of one of the numbers. Choose another team to say which circle number the first team chose. If they are correct, they score a point. Repeat for eighths or three quarters.

Word of the week

Sample tasks
• Fold this sheet of paper into quarters. How many quarters are there?
• Which of the four quarters of this piece of paper is the largest? None, all quarters must be the same size.
• If there are 12 sweets in a pack, how many are there in a quarter?

Sample facts
• there are two quarters in one half
• 5 is one quarter of 20
• one half of a quarter is one eighth

N29 Place-value

Ten pence winner!
Ordering 3-digit numbers
A dice, 10p coins
Draw an 8-division number line on the board, numbered 300, 310, 320, … 370. Draw a HTU grid on the board and write 3 in the hundreds place. Divide the class into two teams.
Choose a child from Team A to throw the dice and write the number in the tens place. Choose another child from Team A to throw the dice and write the number in the units place. Choose a third child from Team A to read the number and write it in the correct position on the number line. Repeat this process for Team B.
The team with a number closest to a multiple of ten collect a 10p coin. Repeat several times. Who collects the most coins?

Bingo
Rounding 2-digit numbers to the nearest ten
Place-value cards (Ts, Us)
Each pair writes five bingo numbers that are multiples of 10 (up to 100). Shuffle the cards separately and place them face down in two piles.
Select a card from each pile and make a 2-digit number, hold it up and say it aloud.
Choose a child to say which ten it rounds to.
Any pair with the matching number can cross it out.

Number of the week

30

Sample tasks	• Which numbers have 30 as their next ten?
	• What must be added to 26, 21, 29, … to make 30?
	• What is our number taken away from 60, 100, 52, …?
Sample facts	• it is the next ten after 24, 27, 21, …
	• it is three 10s, six 5s, two 15s, …
	• it is 22 + 8, 28 + 2, 25 + 5, …
	• it is the number of days in September/ April/ June/ November

N30 Addition/subtraction

Round the class

Adding multiples of 10

A dice

Write a multiple of ten on the board.

Choose a child to throw the dice and add that many tens to the starter number. Write the total on the board.

If correct the first child chooses another to throw the dice and add that many tens to the total.

Continue round the class. How large a total can they make?

Right and wrong

Addition pairs to 100 (multiples of 5)

Write ten additions on the board, some of which are incorrect.

The children work in pairs to 'mark' each addition and decide which are correct.

Point to an addition and choose a pair to say whether or not it is correct.

Repeat for each addition.

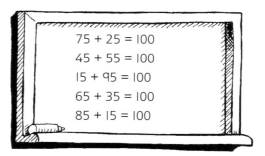

$$75 + 25 = 100$$
$$45 + 55 = 100$$
$$15 + 95 = 100$$
$$65 + 35 = 100$$
$$85 + 15 = 100$$

Shape of the week

triangle

Sample facts
- it is a flat shape (2-d) which has 3 straight sides
- it has 3 corners (vertices)
- drawing a diagonal of a rectangle creates two triangles
- some parts of roofs are triangle shaped (triangular)

N31 Subtraction

Roundabout counting

Counting back in tens from 2- and 3-digit numbers
Cubes
Write ten 3-digit starter numbers on the board.
Point to a starter number. Count back in tens, as a class.
Point to a new starter number. Count back in tens, pointing at random
to different children who say the next number in the count.
If a child says a number with zero tens, they collect a cube.

Ten pence winner!

Subtracting two 2-digit numbers
Place-value cards (1, 2, 3, 4, 5 and 10, 20, 30, 40, 50), 10p coins
Write the numbers '57, 49, 76, 88, 95' on the board.
Divide the class into two teams.
Choose two children from Team A to select a tens and a units card to
make a 2-digit number, e.g. 34. The team choose another, larger, number
from the board (e.g. 57) and subtract the card number from it (e.g.
leaving 23).
Repeat this process for Team B.
The team with an answer closest to 25 win that round and take a 10p
coin.
Repeat several times. Who has the most coins?

Number of the week

Sample tasks	• Count in 10s to/from our number.
	• Double our number/halve our number.
	• Tell me two numbers which add to make our number, e.g. 40 + 30, ...
Sample facts	• it is seven 10s
	• it is 10 more than 60, 20 more than 50, ...
	• it makes 100 with 30

Grid addition

Adding to make the next ten

Draw a 10×2 grid on the board, with a 2-digit number in each space. Children copy the grid, writing how much to make the next ten for each number.

When the grid is complete, point to each space in turn, asking a different child to say their answer, and the next ten.

Show me

Difference

Number cards (1 to 10), one set per pair

Ask the children to show you the number that is the difference between: 3 and 7, 24 and 18, 14 and 18, 19 and 22, 39 and 41, …

Word of the week

Sample tasks
- How many minutes have passed since 11 o'clock?
- How many times can you write your name in a minute?

Sample facts
- a minute is a measure of an amount of time
- there are 60 minutes in 1 hour/30 minutes in half an hour, …
- there are 60 seconds in a minute

N33 Addition

Match me

Adding 9, 19, 29, 39 to 2-digit numbers

Number cards (0 to 9), one set per child

Select two cards at random to make a 2-digit number. Hold it up and read it aloud.

Children add 9, and use two of their cards to match the answer, placing it face up on the table.

Repeat for adding 19, 29 or 39.

Some answers can't be matched – why not?

Missing numbers

Adding 2-digit numbers

Write ten additions on the board, each with the second number missing.

Point to a missing number and choose a child to say what it is.

Repeat for each missing number.

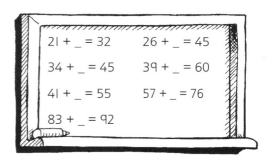

$$21 + \_ = 32 \qquad 26 + \_ = 45$$
$$34 + \_ = 45 \qquad 39 + \_ = 60$$
$$41 + \_ = 55 \qquad 57 + \_ = 76$$
$$83 + \_ = 92$$

Number of the week

31

Sample tasks
- Add our number to 11, 23, 32, 45, ...
- Add 20, 40, 50, 30, ... to our number.
- The tens digit of our number is two more than its units digit. What other numbers are like this?

Sample facts
- its digits are both odd
- it is 1 more than double 15
- it is the number of days in January, March, May, July, ...

 **Addition**

Target counting

Counting in tens from a 3-digit number

A dice

Write a 3-digit target number on the board, e.g. 482.

Throw the dice twice to give the hundreds and the tens of the starter number. Use the units of the target number to complete it.

Children decide whether to count forwards or backwards from the starter to the target.

Count in tens in unison to the target number.

Repeat, counting around the class, pointing at random to the next child.

Bingo

Adding 1-digit and 2-digit numbers

Number cards (20 to 50)

Each pair writes six 2-digit numbers between 25 and 56.

Choose a child to select a card at random and read it aloud. Choose another to throw the dice. Choose a third child to add the two – check with the class.

Any pair with the matching total can cross it out.

The first pair to cross out three of their numbers wins.

Shape of the week

cylinder

Sample facts
- it is a solid or hollow (3-d) shape
- its two ends are circles (circular)
- it has two flat faces and one curved face
- a tube is a cylinder
- it is a prism with circle (circular) ends

N35 Addition/subtraction

People numbers

Counting in hundreds from a 3-digit number

Stick a 3-digit number on the back of a child, e.g. 484. Write the tens and units on the board, i.e. 84.

As a class, count in unison in hundreds from the board number up to the target. When the children reach the target they should stand up. The first child writes the number on the board. Unpin the number – are they correct?

Grid addition

Adding 50 to 3-digit numbers

Draw a 5 × 2 grid on the board, with a 3-digit number in each space. Children copy the grid, writing the numbers 50 more.

When the grid is complete, point to each space in turn, asking a different child to say their answer.

Number of the week

Sample tasks
- What must be added to 30, 90, 50, ... to make our number?
- How many 10s is our number? How many 20s, 25s, 50s, ...?
- Take our number away from 240, 360, 490, ...

Sample facts
- it is a century
- it is the first 3-digit number
- it can make a square with 10 rows of 10

N36 Numbers to 1000

Guess the number

Counting in hundreds, tens, units

Choose a child and stick a 3-digit target number on her back, e.g. 563. She writes a 2-digit starter number on the board, e.g. 28. The class count on in hundreds until they reach a number with the same number of hundreds as the target (i.e. 528). The first child writes this number on the board. She asks: *Is my number larger or smaller than this?*
The class count on or back in tens until they reach a number with the same number of tens as the target (i.e. 568).
The first child writes this number on the board. She asks: *Is my number larger or smaller than this?* The class count on or back in ones until they reach the target (563). The first child writes this on the board. Compare with the number on her back – is she correct? Repeat.

Number chains

Even and odd numbers

Write five sequences of even or odd numbers on the board, each with some numbers missing. Point to a missing number and choose a child to say what it is. Repeat for each missing number.

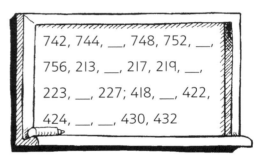

742, 744, __, 748, 752, __,
756, 213, __, 217, 219, __,
223, __, 227; 418, __, 422,
424, __, __, 430, 432

Word of the week

sequence

Sample tasks
- What are the next numbers in this sequence: 1, 4, 7, 10, ...?
- Tell me the first five numbers in the sequence of odd numbers.

Sample facts
- the sequence: 5, 10, 15, 20, ...is made by counting in 5s
- the missing number in this sequence: 1, 3, 5, _ , 9, 11, ... is 7

N37 Multiplication/division

Open the box

Multiplying by 10

Draw a 5 × 2 grid on the board. Cover each space
with a 2-digit number, and underneath write
that number multiplied by 10.
Choose a child to point to a box and multiply
by 10. Check with the class.
The child can 'open the box' to reveal the
answer.

Guess my number

×5 and ×10 multiplication facts, addition

Write '8, 9, 4, 7' on the board.
In each pair, one child selects a number from the board, multiplies
either by 5 or 10, then adds a different number from the board.
They write the result, and their partner must work out which was their
starting number.
Repeat, swapping roles.

Number of the week

Sample tasks
- Say three numbers which add to our number, e.g.
  30 + 40 + 20.
- Take away 40, 20, 80, 50, ... from our number.
- Count in 5s to/from our number.

Sample facts
- it is three 30s, nine 10s, ...
- it is 10 less than 100
- it is between 85 and 95

Match me

Multiplication facts up to 10 × 10

Number cards (0 to 9), one set per child and (1 to 9) for the teacher

Select two cards at random and hold them up.
The children use cards to match the result of multiplying one number
by the other, placing it face up on the table.

Open the box

×10 and ×100 multiplication facts

Draw a 5 × 2 grid on the board. Cover each space with
a number (1 to 10), and underneath write the
matching multiple of 10.

Choose a child to point to a box and multiply by 10.
Check with the class.
The child can 'open the box' to reveal the answer.
Repeat for multiplying by 100.

Word of the week

multiple

Sample tasks
- Tell me a multiple of 3.
- What are the first five multiples of 10?
- Is 9 a multiple of 2?

Sample facts
- the multiples of 2 are the even numbers
- the first five multiples of 5 are 5, 10, 15, 20, 25
- 100 is a multiple of 10

ⓝ39 Multiplication/division

Missing number

Counting in twos

Write five sequences of multiples of 2 on the board, each with several numbers missing.
Point to a missing number and choose a child to say what it is.
Repeat for each missing number.

Right or wrong

Doubling

Write ten numbers and their doubles on the board. Ensure that several of the doubles are incorrect.
Point to a double and choose a child to say whether or not it is correct.
Repeat for each double.

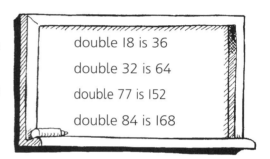

double 18 is 36

double 32 is 64

double 77 is 152

double 84 is 168

Number of the week

36

Sample tasks
- Count in 2s, 3s, 4s, 6s to our number.
- How many 3s make our number? How many 4s, 6s,..?
- One digit is double the other. What other numbers are like this?

Sample facts
- it is 4 less than 40, 14 less than 50, 24 less than 60, ...
- it can be divided by 2, by 3, by 4, by 6, by 9, by 12, by 18, by 36
- it is six 6s (a square number)

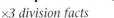 **N40** Multiplication/division

Stand up!

Multiplication facts up to 6 × 6
Number cards (2 to 6), 10p coins
Each child writes any multiplication
fact on a piece of paper
(up to 6 × 6).
Select a number card at random,
hold it up and say it aloud, e.g. *four.*
Start chanting that table, in unison:
one four is four, two fours are eight, ...
Any child with a matching fact
stands up when it is said.
They collect a coin if they are
correct.

Six questions

×3 division facts
Cubes
Read out six division facts (in the ×3 table) quickly:

> *How many threes in nine?*
> *How many threes in eighteen? etc.*

Children write the answers.
Ask different pairs for their answers. Each pair marks their own work.
Any pair with all six correct collects a cube.
Repeat.

Shape of the week

Sample facts
- it is a solid or hollow (3-d) shape
- it has 2 flat ends which are the same shape
- if the ends are triangles it is called a triangular prism
- if the ends are squares or rectangles, the prism is
  a cuboid
- many boxes are prism shaped

(N41) Fractions

Grid fractions

Halves, quarters, thirds
Draw a 6×2 grid, with a 2-digit
number in each space.
Children copy the grid,
finding half of the first
number, one third of the
second, one quarter of
the third, then half of
the next, ...
When the grid is
complete, point to
each space in turn,
asking a different
child to say their answer.

How many?

Halving
Write '48, 64, 80' on the board.
The children find how many times they can halve each number (until
they reach an odd number).
Allow five minutes.
Discuss their answers.

Number of the week

Sample tasks
- Count in $\frac{1}{2}$s from our number, i.e. $\frac{1}{2}$, 1, $1\frac{1}{2}$, 2, ...
- What is $\frac{1}{2}$ of 4, 10, 14, 20, ...?
- Which numbers have these as halves: 3, 6, 2, 7, ...?

Sample facts
- it is a fraction – two of them make one whole
- $\frac{1}{2}$ of an hour is 30 minutes
- $\frac{1}{2}$ of £1 is 50p

(N42) Addition

Right and wrong

Adding 9 or 19 to a 2-digit number

Choose a child to add 36 and 19 on the board, focusing on adding 20 and taking away 1. Write ten additions on the board of a 2-digit number and 9 or 19, one of which is incorrect.

$34 + 19 = 53$ $77 + 19 = 96$
$25 + 9 = 34$ $55 + 9 = 64$
$37 + 9 = 46$ $29 + 19 = 48$
$42 + 19 = 63$ $48 + 9 = 57$
$83 + 9 = 92$ $62 + 19 = 81$

Allow children five minutes to decide which addition is incorrect.

Target number

Adding 21, 32, 43 to a 3-digit number

Each pair writes a 3-digit number. Write a 2-digit number on the board (21, 32 or 43).
Each pair adds the 2-digit to the 3-digit number.
Write a 3-digit multiple of ten on the board, e.g. 400.
The pair with the closest answer scores a point.

Word of the week

horizontal

Sample tasks
- Draw me a horizontal line on the board.
- Tell me a horizontal pair of numbers on this number grid (1 to 100).
- Hold your ruler horizontally.

Sample facts
- a horizontal line goes across the board from left to right
- the horizon is horizontal
- I can lie on the floor horizontally

(N43) Addition

Bingo

Adding three 1-digit numbers.

Number cards (2 to 10)

Each pair writes five bingo numbers that are between 9 and 27.
Select three cards at random, hold them up and say them aloud.
Choose a child to say the total.
Any pair with the matching number can cross it out.

People numbers

Adding three multiples of ten

Choose three children and stick a multiple of ten on the back of each.
The class add the three numbers and say the answer.
The three children must guess their numbers.

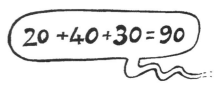

Number of the week

Sample tasks
- Add our number to 20, 32, 54, ... by adding 20, then taking 1 away.
- Take our number from 45, 63, 35, ... by taking away 20, then adding 1.
- What must be added to our number to make 100, 50, 200, ...?

Sample facts
- its nearest ten is 20
- its digits have a difference of 8
- it is the largest 'teen' number

Activity Bank

The Activity Bank includes a variety of activities that address key skills. The activities in the bank can be used at any time alongside any topic, and often you will wish to revisit them throughout the year.

The table lists each activity in the bank, along with the key skill addressed, to help your selection.

Activity	Skill
Place-value, ordering, estimating, rounding	
Guess my number	3-digit numbers
Number guess	Ordering 3-digit numbers
Largest number	Place-value in 4-digit numbers
Start and stop	Counting in ones
Change-over	Counting in tens
Group counting	Counting in hundreds
Open the box	Rounding 2-digit numbers to the nearest ten
Missing numbers	Rounding 3-digit numbers to the nearest ten
Number line	Rounding 3-digit numbers to the nearest hundred

Activity	Skill
Addition and subtraction	
Card pairs	Addition pairs for numbers up to 10
Guess the card	Addition pairs to 20
Turn it over	Addition pairs to 100 Addition pairs to 1000
Addition and subtraction patterns	Adding and subtracting 1-digit numbers
How much now?	Adding 9 to a 2-digit number
Bingo	Adding three 1-digit numbers
Number guess	Adding multiples of ten to 2-digit numbers
Shout about it!	Adding 9, 19, 29, ... to 2-digit numbers
Running total	Adding 11, 21, 31, ... to 2-digit numbers

| Team effort | Subtracting multiples of 10 |
| People numbers | Subtracting 9, 19, 29, ... from a 2-digit number |

Multiplication and division	
Play again	Doubling numbers up to 20
Four in a row	Doubling multiples of 5 to 50
	Doubling multiples of 50 to 500
Turn it over	Halving even numbers to 20
Team up	Halving multiples of 10 to 100
Running count	Counting in twos
Missing numbers	Counting in threes
	Counting in fours
Home and safe	Counting in fours
Shout about it!	Counting in fives
Counting in tens	Counting in tens
Pair it off!	×3 multiplication and division facts
Four in a row	×4 multiplication and division facts
Towers	×5 multiplication and division facts
Shout about it!	Multiplication facts

Solving problems in real life and measures	
Pocket money savings	Solving problems involving money
Is it different?	Solving problems involving money
Change it	Solving problems involving money
Lots of pennies!	Solving problems involving money
Few as possible	Solving problems involving money
Growing pains	Solving problems involving measures
Furniture fun	Solving problems involving measures
Later and earlier	Solving problems involving time
Cake count-up	Solving problems involving time
Minutes of sleep	Solving problems involving time
Termly days	Solving problems involving time
Football fun	Solving problems involving time

① Place-value, ordering, estimating, rounding

Guess my number

3-digit numbers

The class play as a team against you. Tell the children you are thinking of a 3-digit number. Choose different children to ask a question to help the class guess what it is.

If after five questions the class guess incorrectly you score a point. If they guess correctly they score a point.

Who is the first to 10 points?

Number guess

Ordering 3-digit numbers

The pairs write a 3-digit number, hidden from everyone else.

Write a 3-digit starter number on the board. Choose a pair and ask if their number is higher or lower than the starter number. When they have answered ask the class to guess what their number might be. They say 'higher' or 'lower'. Continue until the class have guessed their number.

Repeat for a different pair.

Largest number

Place-value in 4-digit numbers

A dice

Divide the class into two or three teams.

Draw a place-value grid on the board for each team, with space for thousands, hundreds, tens and units.

Each team takes a turn to throw the dice. After each throw they decide where on their grid to place the digit. They are trying to make the largest number they can. Once a number has been placed it can't be moved.

After four rounds who has the largest number? That team scores a point. Repeat, with each team trying to make the smallest number they can.

Start and stop

Counting in ones

In unison, chant in ones starting at a given number, e.g. 134.

Point to a child, who stops counting – the rest of the class continue. Point to another child, then another, … until only about five children are still counting.

Point to a child who starts counting again. Point to another, then another, … until the whole class are once more counting in unison.

Change-over

Counting in tens

In unison, count in tens from a 2-digit number. After a short while stop the count. Point to a child who stands up and continues the count alone. Point to another child who stands up and takes over the count (the first child sits down). Continue like this around the class.
Practise over time so that the change-overs are smooth.

Group counting

Counting in hundreds

The children work in groups of four or five – you can give each group a team name, e.g. tigers, lions, elephants, …
Start counting in hundreds from a given number. Point to a team who take over the count. Point to a different team who take over the count. Continue around the groups.
Variation: Each team chooses the next group to take over the count.

Open the box

Rounding 2-digit numbers to the nearest ten

Draw a 4×2 grid. Cover each space with a 2-digit number (e.g. 47), and underneath write the nearest ten (i.e. 50).
Choose a child to point to a box and round it to the nearest ten. Check with the class.
The child can 'open the box' to reveal the answer.

Missing numbers

Rounding 3-digit numbers to the nearest ten
Write several 3-digit numbers on the board, rounding each to the
nearest ten, but missing a digit from the answer.
794 → 7_0, 612 → 6_0, 538 → 5_0, 446 → 4_0, 313 → 3_0 , 215 → 2_0
743 → 74_, 503 → 5_0, 109 → 1_0
Point to a number with a missing digit and choose a child to tell you
what it is.
Repeat for each number.

Number line 🗣️

Rounding 3-digit numbers to the nearest hundred
Choose ten children and label each one with a multiple of 100.
Ask the ten children to count along the line, each one saying their
number.
Each pair writes any 3-digit number.
Each pair in turn says their number then rounds it to the nearest
hundred. They give their number to that child in the line.

❷ Addition and subtraction

Card pairs 🗣

Addition pairs for numbers up to 10
Sets of number cards (0 to 9)
The children work in pairs, each with a set of number cards.
Write '9' on the board. Each pair chooses two cards that total 9,
e.g. 4 and 5.
Say *Show me!* Each pair holds up their cards, facing you. Choose
different pairs to read out their numbers.
Repeat for other pairs for numbers up to 10, maintaining a lively pace.

Guess the card

Addition pairs to 20
Number cards (0 to 20)
Choose two children and give one of them the set of number cards. That
child chooses a card (e.g. 7) and shows you and the other child, but
no-one else. The second child says the pair to make 20, e.g. thirteen.
The rest of the class have to guess the number on the card. Reveal the
card. Were they correct?
Repeat with different children.

Turn it over

Addition pairs to 100

Two blank pieces of card per child, number cards (5, 10, 15, ... 100)

Each child writes two multiples of 5 between 5 and 100 on their cards and turns them face down.

Select a number card at random and read it aloud. What goes with this number to make 100? The children decide if they can turn over one of their cards to match the answer.

Continue until most children have turned over both cards.

Repeat.

Turn it over

Addition pairs to 1000

Repeat the above activity for pairs of multiples of 100 that make 1000.

Addition and subtraction patterns

Adding and subtracting 1-digit numbers
Write the numbers 1 to 9 on the board.
The pairs combine the numbers in the given order, using a pattern, e.g. add, add, subtract, add, add, subtract, ... (i.e. $1 + 2 + 3 - 4 + 5 + 6 - 7 + 8 + 9$).
What is the final result?
Repeat for a different patterns, e.g. add, add, add, subtract, subtract, ...

How much now?

Adding 9 to a 2-digit number
A selection of coins
Show the children an amount of money (up to about 60p). *How much do I have?* Each pair writes the amount.
Tell the children you have an extra 9p in your pocket. *What is the total now?*
Take some suggestions, then choose a pair to complete the addition on the board.
Repeat for different amounts.

Bingo

Adding three 1-digit numbers
Each pair writes five bingo numbers that are between 10 and 27
Write an addition on the board, e.g. $6 + 5 + 4 =$. Point out the two numbers that add to make 10, and choose a child to say the total.
Any pair with the matching number can cross it out.
Repeat for other additions of three numbers, where two add to make 10.

Number guess

Adding multiples of ten to 2-digit numbers

A dice

Each child writes down a 2-digit number (more than 60), hidden from everyone else.

Choose a child to throw the dice and subtract that many tens from their number, saying the answer.

The others guess the original number.

Shout about it!

Adding 9, 19, 29, ... to 2-digit numbers

Number cards (0 to 9), interlocking cubes

Each child writes a 2-digit number. Write a near-multiple of ten on the board, e.g. 29.

The children add your number and their number. Select a card at random and hold it up. Any child with this number of units in their answer shouts *Snap!*. Check their answer with the class. Any children who are correct can take a cube.

Repeat, for different numbers.

Running total

Adding 11, 21, 31, ... to 2-digit numbers

Interlocking cubes

Choose a child to write a 2-digit starter number on the board.

Write 11, 21 or 31 on the board (you choose). The pairs work to add that number to the starter number as many times as they can. Stop them after a few minutes.

Choose some pairs to write their totals on the board.

Check with the class that the totals are correct by completing the additions on the board.

Any pair with a correct total collect a cube. The pair with the largest total collect three cubes.

Repeat for different numbers.

Team effort

Subtracting multiples of 10

Two dice

Divide the class into four or five teams. Each team writes three 2-digit numbers (all with fewer than six units) on a large poster and pegs it up. Throw the dice three times to make a 3-digit number, e.g. 364. Choose a multiple of ten, e.g. 20.

Point to a team. They subtract 20 from the 3-digit number and write the answer. Point to another team who subtract another 20 and write the answer. Continue pointing to different teams who subtract 20 and write the answer, until you reach a 1-digit or 'teens' number. Any team with a number in the sequence can cross it out.

Repeat. The first team to cross all three numbers off their poster, wins.

People numbers

Subtracting 9, 19, 29, … from a 2-digit number

Number cards (9, 19, 29)

Choose five children and pin a 2-digit number (more than 30) to the back of each.

Choose a child to select a number card at random. They point to one of the children with a number and subtract the number card from the pinned number.

The pinned child must guess what their number is.

Repeat for each child.

❸ Multiplication and division

Play again

Doubling numbers up to 20

Lots of £1 coins

The children each write three even numbers between 2 and 40.
Choose a child to write a number between 1 and 20 on the board. They choose a second child to double the number. If the answer matches one of the second child's numbers they collect a coin. If not, they write a new number between 1 and 20 on the board and choose a new child to double it.
Continue for several rounds. Who has the most coins?

Four in a row

Doubling multiples of 5 to 50

Draw a 5 × 5 grid on the board, and write a multiple of 10 (up to 100) in each space (most multiples should appear at least twice).
Each pair writes a multiple of five between 5 and 50. Choose a pair to double their number and cross out the answer on the grid (if they can).
Continue around the pairs until all the numbers have been crossed out.
Any pair who cross out a number to complete a row or column get a cheer!

Four in a row

Doubling multiples of 50 to 500
Repeat the above activity for multiples of 50.

Turn it over

Halving even numbers to 20
Two blank pieces of card per child, number cards (2, 4, 6, ... 20)
Each child writes two 1-digit numbers on their cards and turns them face down.
Select a number card at random and read it aloud. *What is half of this number?* The children decide if they can turn over one of their cards to match the answer.
Continue until most children have turned over both cards.
Repeat.

Team up

Halving multiples of 10 to 100
Divide the class into two teams. Write the multiples of ten up to 200 on the board.
Choose a team. They nominate a child to quickly write half of one of the multiples below it. Check with the whole class whether the halving is correct. If so, that team scores a point. Repeat, swapping between teams until all the multiples have been halved.
Which team has the most points?

Running count

Counting in twos

Cubes

Choose a child to write a 2-digit starter number on the board.

The pairs count on in twos, writing each number, as far as they can. Stop them after a few minutes. What numbers have they reached? Write some on the board.

Check with the class that the numbers are correct by counting in twos and keeping a running total.

Any pair with a correct number collect a cube. The pair with the largest number collect three cubes.

Repeat for different numbers.

Missing numbers

Counting in threes

Write six sequences on the board, counting in threes, each with some numbers missing.

Point to a missing number and choose a child to say what it is.

Repeat for each missing number.

Missing numbers

Counting in fours

Repeat the above activity for sequences of fours.

Home and safe

Counting in fours

Each child writes a multiple of four. As a class, count in fours from four. As each child's number is said they stand up. How far do you have to count before everyone is standing up? Count back down. As their number is said each child sits down.

Shout about it!

Counting in fives

Number cards (1 to 20), interlocking cubes

Each child writes a 2-digit multiple of five (e.g. 35).

Write a number between 1 and 20 on the board, e.g. 9. Each child counts on that many fives from their number, and writes the total (e.g. 35, 40, 45, 50, 55, 60, 65, 70, 75, 80).

Select a number card, write that many tens on the board and add five units (e.g. choose card 14, write 145). Any child with the matching total shouts *Snap!*. Check their answer. If they are correct they collect a cube. Repeat, starting with different numbers.

Counting in tens

Counting in tens
Write ten 2- and 3-digit multiples of ten on the board.
Point to a starter number. Count on in tens as a class.
Point to a new starter number. Count on in tens, pointing at random to
different children who say the next number in the count.
Repeat for numbers that are not multiples of ten.

Pair it off!

×3 multiplication and division facts
Divide the class into two teams.
In Team A each child writes a multiple of 3 up to 36. In Team B each child
writes a number from 1 to 12.
On your mark the children find a partner from the opposite team to make
a ×3 multiplication or division fact (e.g. 4 goes with 12, 8 with 24). Some
children will have several partners.
Check each set is correct. The
children in each set write their
matching multiplication and
division on the board.

Four in a row 🗣

×4 multiplication and division facts

Draw a 5 × 5 grid on the board, and write a multiple of 4 (up to 48) in each space (most multiples should appear at least twice).

Each pair writes a number from 1 to 12. Choose a pair to multiply their number by 4 and cross out the answer on the grid (if they can). Continue around the pairs until all the numbers have been crossed out. Any pair who cross out a number to complete a row or column get a cheer!

Towers 🗣

×5 multiplication and division facts

Each pair writes a 1-digit number on a piece of paper and passes it to the next pair. Each pair multiplies their new number by 5, writes the answer, and passes it on to the next pair. Each pair checks the new multiplication. Any pairs who are correct collect a cube.

Repeat until one pair has a tower of five cubes.

Shout about it!

Multiplication facts

A dice, interlocking cubes

Each child writes a multiple of 2, 3, 4 or 5 or 6. Write a starter number
between 1 and 10 on the board, e.g. 9.

Throw the dice and write the number on the board, e.g. 4. Choose a child
to multiply the dice number by the starter number and say the answer
($4 \times 9 = 36$). Any child with a matching number shouts *Snap!*. Check their
multiplication. Any child who is correct collects a cube.

Repeat starting with different numbers.

④ Solving problems in real life and measures

Pocket money savings

Solving problems involving money

Write '75p' on the board.

Address the class: *Suppose you get this much pocket money each week. How many weeks until you save £10?*

Allow the pairs a few minutes to discuss and agree an answer.

Discuss it as a class, working out a week-by-week total. Which pairs were closest?

Is it different?

Solving problems involving money

Address the class: *How many different amounts can you make if you use four different coins?*

Allow the pairs five minutes to discuss the problem. Discuss how you might set about checking that you have them all, e.g. 1p + 2p + 5p + 10p, and 2p + 5p + 10p + 20p, ... and so on.

Allow the pairs another five minutes.

Change it

Solving problems involving money
Draw five toys on the board, labelled with prices: 45p, 27p, 36p, 52p, 18p.
Address the class: *You can only pay for each toy using one coin. What is the smallest amount of change you will receive for each toy?*
Allow the pairs a few minutes to work on the problem. Discuss each one with the class.
Repeat using different prices.

Lots of pennies!

Solving problems involving money
Draw five money boxes on the board, labelled with amounts: £1.83, £2.20, £1.97, £4.44, £5.03.
Address the class: *These children have saved their pennies. Each box only has penny coins in it. How many pennies in each money box?*
The children write down their answers. Discuss each one with the class.
Repeat for different amounts.

Few as possible

Solving problems involving money
Selection of coins
Write these amounts on the board: 45p, 73p, 81p, £1.33p, 39p, £2.90p, 23p.
Each pair chooses an amount, and decides which are the fewest coins needed to match it. They record the coins they need.
Show a coin to the class. Each pair puts up their hand if they have used this coin. Check that they are correct. Continue, holding up different coins.

Growing pains

Solving problems involving measures

Write '125 g' on the board.

Address the class: *Suppose a baby puts on this much weight each week. Its weight now is 3 kg. How many weeks until it weighs 8 kg?*

Allow the pairs a few minutes to discuss and agree an answer.

Discuss it as a class, working out a week-by-week weight. Which pairs were closest?

Furniture fun

Solving problems involving measures

Draw five bookcases on the board, labelled with lengths: 58 cm, 102 cm, 37 cm, 99 cm, 80 cm.

Address the class: *You have space for bookcases of total length 2 m. What different combinations of bookcase could you buy?*

Allow the pairs a few minutes to work on the problem, then discuss the answers as a class.

Later and earlier

Solving problems involving time
Write these times on the board. 3:45, 2:15, 7:35, 5:55, 6:30, 8:25.
The pairs choose a time and answer four questions:
What was the time one hour earlier?
What will be the time 30 minutes later?
What was the time 5 minutes earlier?
What will be the time 10 minutes later?
Discuss each time and the answers with the class.

Cake count-up

Solving problems involving time
Draw four cakes on the board. Label each cake with a 'start cooking' and an 'end cooking' time.
How long does each cake cook? If each cake needs five minutes more, what time will it finish cooking?
Allow the pairs a few minutes to agree an answer.
Discuss the answers with the class.

Minutes of sleep

Solving problems involving time
Address the class: *The average child sleeps ten hours. How many minutes sleep is that?* Challenge each pair of children to calculate how many hours and minutes they sleep.

Termly days

Solving problems involving time

On the board write the term start and end dates.

Address the class: *How many days do we spend at school (i.e. not including weekends)?*

Allow the pairs a few minutes to agree an answer, then discuss as a whole class.

Football fun

Solving problems involving time

Address the class: *Two teams are playing in a cup final. There is 45 minutes play each way. There is a break of 15 minutes between halves. There is 5 minutes injury time. But the match is a draw! They have to have a play an extra 15 minutes each way. How long does the whole match last in minutes and in hours?*

Allow the children a few minutes to agree and answer, then discuss as a whole class.